AC1   D
TRAVEL GAMES

Compiled by The Puzzle House
Illustrated by Barry Green

Henderson
Woodbridge, England *Publishing*

INTRODUCTION

There are lots of games, puzzles, jokes and activities in this book. They are designed to help you through those boring bits that are bound to happen on any journey . . . and you can tackle them whether in a car, on a boat, a train or a plane (but don't try them on the back of your bike).

Some things you can tackle on your own, some with one friend and some are best suited to as many people as possible.

REMEMBER

If you are in a car the driver CANNOT get involved in anything that involves him or her taking eyes off the road or losing concentration in any way.

If you are travelling with lots of fellow passengers have a thought for them . . . not everyone wants to sing verse five thousand and sixty three of 'One Man Went To Mow'.

USEFUL THINGS TO TAKE ON A JOURNEY

This book (a must!)

Plain paper

Pocket-size notebook

Pencil (not too sharp. HB/1B or 2B are best)

Pencil sharpener

Maps (when you are travelling over land)

1 UNTIDY SUITCASE

The things in the suitcase are in a bit of a jumble. Can you sort them out?

1 A E I N R R S T
2 A C I K R S T T U
3 A E J N S
4 I I M S S T U W
5 A E H I R S S T T W

2 RED FOR DANGER

Here's a railway sign. How many R's in it?

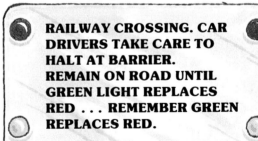

RAILWAY CROSSING. CAR
DRIVERS TAKE CARE TO
HALT AT BARRIER.
REMAIN ON ROAD UNTIL
GREEN LIGHT REPLACES
RED . . . REMEMBER GREEN
REPLACES RED.

TRANS-FACTS
In 1987, 46 Australians went for a bike
ride — on one machine!

3 JOURNEY LOG

Make a record of all the things that happen on your journey. Use the pages of a lined notebook. Your info will be different depending on whether you are on a two hour car journey or a five day boat trip . . . but here's a list of suggestions for things to note down.

DATES AND TIMES

DATE OF JOURNEY

TIME OF DEPARTURE

TIME OF ARRIVAL

Before setting off you will have an idea of when you hope to arrive. Note this down and see how close you were to the actual arrival time.

If you are in a car then you can add info taken from the dashboard, such as speed of travel. On any journey you can make hourly notes of place names you have reached. Airlines provide detailed info about the height and speed of the craft.

Weather:
Use a set of symbols (sun, rainclouds etc) to record the weather throughout the trip.

Things of interest:
Important buildings or places seen:
  Palaces, museums, sporting venues, theme parks, nature reserves
Geographical features seen:
  Mountains, lakes, rivers, forests
Friends or famous people seen:
  (Perhaps all your friends ARE famous people)

DAD IF YOU CAN'T FIND THE M6 MOTORWAY THEN WHY DON'T WE GO UP THE M3 TWICE?

HOW WOULD YOU LIKE TO WALK?

TRANS-FACTS
Traffic congestion in Hong Kong is five times greater than in the UK.

4 START THE CAR

That's how most journeys begin. Find an answer to the quick clues that always begin with the letters **C A R**

1 It lets air into a petrol engine

C A R _ _ _ _ _ _ _ _ _

2 Sea between W Indies and America

C A R _ _ _ _ _ _

3 Type of toffee

C A R _ _ _ _

4 House on wheels

C A R _ _ _ _

5 Knitted woollen jacket

C A R _ _ _ _ _

6 Moving drawing

C A R _ _ _ _

7 Festival or fair

C A R _ _ _ _ _

8 Part of a train

C A R _ _ _ _ _

9 Transport, lift

C A R _ _

10 Two-wheeled vehicle pulled by horse

C A R _

5 SPOT THE DIFFERENCE

There are SIX differences between the two pictures. Can you spot the lot?

Each letter which slots into the frame has a number. We have given you two words with their number codes to start you off. Keep a record of which number represents which letter in the smaller grid, and find the words to fit the frame.

5	21	5	18	14	8		12		20	
4		25		3	23	5	4	15	5	
19	5	1	3	11	14		2		4	
6		10		5		1 P	2 L	3 A	4 N	5 E
4		11 R	15 U	8 S	8 S	6 I	3 A		5	
16	5	14		10		7		3	2	1
	22		12	11	3	7	6	2		6
19	15	23	5	14		3		13		16
	3		16		3	8	9	10	11	5
3	2	24	3	26	8			8		10
	8		4		17	6	14	14	5	4

1	2	3	4	5	6	7	8	9	10	11	12	13
P	L	A	N	E	I		S			R		
14	**15**	**16**	**17**	**18**	**19**	**20**	**21**	**22**	**23**	**24**	**25**	**26**
	U											

TRANS-FACTS
The Penny Farthing bicycle with one large front wheel and one small rear one was — for some reason — also known as the Ordinary Bicycle.

7 STOP GAP

Fill in the gaps in the words by using a word of three letters. Use the same word for the three examples in each group.

CLUE — each three-letter word has something to do with travel or transport

1 _ _ _ INESS   3 _ _ _ _ SON
   AM _ _ _ H   SWAN _ _ _
   _ _ _ TLE   DI _ _ _ SE

2 _ _ _ PET
   S _ _ _ LET
   S _ _ _ ED

8 PLACEGRAMS

Rearrange the letters in the words below to make the names of cities and towns around the world

1 HASTEN _____

2 ROVED _____

3 DOESNT _____

4 PAIRS _____

5 MORE _____

9 SPY-IT SCORE-IT

A spotter game where you decide that certain objects are worth a certain number of points. Each time you spy the object you score the points. You can adapt this game to any form of travel. Here are some examples.

On a boat
Aeroplane scores 1
Ship scores 3
Coastline scores 6

In a car
Traffic light scores 1
Church scores 3
Telephone box 6

In a plane
Town scores 1
Lake scores 3
Airport scores 6

In a train
Cow scores 1
Bridge scores 3
Ice cream van scores 6

WHAT'S BIG, HAIRY AND FLIES AT 2,000 MPH?

UMMM...I SPY

MUST BE KING KONGCORD

TRANS-FACTS
Peking railway station has a waiting room which will hold 14,000 people.

10 WHEELIE?

How many wheels are there in the drawing?

11 TRACK TO CHINA

How do you find the track to China? Answer, through this word puzzle. Start with the word TRACK, then change a letter at a time making a new word with each move until you reach CHINA. Use the clues to help you find the in-between words.

T R A C K

_ _ _ _ _   **Done by a magician**

_ _ _ _ _   **Opposite of thin**

_ _ _ _ _   **Young hen**

_ _ _ _ _   **Thin strip of light**

C H I N A

Search out the names with a flying link in the word square. Words appear in straight lines across, back, up, down or diagonally. You can use letters more than once but you don't have to use them all.

AEROPLANE	FIN	PASSENGERS
AIRLINE	FLAP	PILOT
BAG HANDLER	GALLEY	RUNWAY
CABIN	HELICOPTER	STEWARDESS
CONCORDE	HOVERCRAFT	TICKET
CREW	JET	TOWER
CUSHION	JUMBO	WING
DECK	LOUNGE	

S	C	U	S	H	I	O	N	T	F	A	I
R	T	O	L	I	P	O	T	I	K	J	T
L	I	E	I	R	P	R	N	C	B	E	C
N	P	A	W	G	P	N	E	K	O	A	C
B	A	G	H	A	N	D	L	E	R	O	C
H	S	R	L	L	R	D	E	T	C	R	O
O	S	F	O	L	N	D	A	C	E	E	N
V	E	O	R	E	D	E	E	W	C	T	C
E	N	O	N	Y	C	G	R	S	O	P	O
R	G	T	R	D	N	U	O	G	S	O	R
C	E	E	O	U	N	B	P	C	N	C	D
R	R	O	O	W	M	T	L	N	C	I	E
A	S	L	A	U	E	D	A	R	O	L	W
F	E	Y	J	J	C	R	N	O	N	E	C
T	A	I	R	L	I	N	E	O	R	H	D

13 OFF THE RAILS

This is a plan of connecting railway lines. The easiest way to get from Newtown to Old Town is to go in a straight line, calling at TWO stations on the way. But can you find a route from Newtown to Old Town in which you pass through an ODD Number of stations on the way?

NEWTOWN   OLD TOWN

TRANS-FACTS
The fare on the Moscow Underground has not changed since 1935 when it was first opened.

14 COLOUR I-SPY

An old favourite is I-SPY, where the players have to guess an object after being given the starter letter. For a change, why not try out COLOUR I-SPY? The first player chooses an object that he can see, but instead of naming the first letter says the COLOUR OF THE OBJECT. As in the alphabet game, the person who guesses correctly then becomes the spy. This is a good game for younger children who aren't that accurate with their spelling. (When you've spent 20 minutes spying for something beginning with K only to be told that it was 'cow' you do tend to lose interest!)

A HUMAN... THAT'S ANOTHER POINT TO ME

TRANS-FACTS
In February 1980, France experienced a traffic jam over 100 miles long.

15 ROUNDABOUT THE UK

Find the names of five UK towns in the circle below. The last letter of one name is the first of the next.

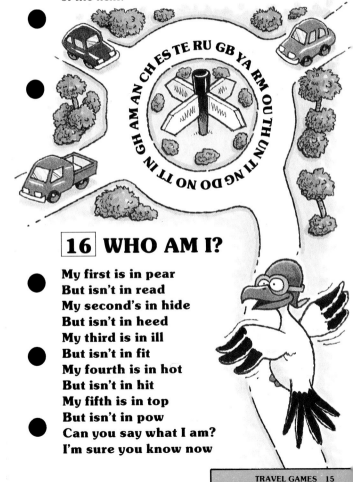

16 WHO AM I?

My first is in pear
But isn't in read
My second's in hide
But isn't in heed
My third is in ill
But isn't in fit
My fourth is in hot
But isn't in hit
My fifth is in top
But isn't in pow
Can you say what I am?
I'm sure you know now

Each group of ten letters can be broken down into TWO words of five letters. Words read from left to right and the letters are in the correct order. Can you make the break? There's a clue in each case

1 LCIBHYIANA

_ _ _ _ _ / _ _ _ _ _

Two countries

2 CIBOIRZFAU

_ _ _ _ _ / _ _ _ _ _

Two islands, favourite holiday places

3 PAMIRLISAN

_ _ _ _ _ / _ _ _ _ _

Two European cities

18 I PACKED MY BAG

An old-favourite memory game that's been played since . . . er, sorry, can't remember. Will adapt as a patience game, but is much more fun with a few people playing.

The first player begins by saying aloud, "I packed my bag and I put in my 'Eat Porridge For Breakfast' T-shirt". The next player then repeats the sentence but adds another object eg: "I packed my bag and I put in my 'Eat Porridge For Breakfast' T-shirt and a clock with only one finger". Players take turns to repeat the sentence, adding on something different each time.

. . . I PACKED MY BAG BACKWARDS

The same game but different. In fact it is played going backwards . . . not when you are travelling backwards, but it's the first game in reverse. Best used with all players having pencil and paper.

One person reads out a long list of things packed in the bag. (It could be the list at the end of the previous game.) Then, after a short pause the list is read out again BUT ONE ITEM is left out. Each player has to write down the item they think was left out. The person with the list reads through the objects again and another item is left out. This goes on until there is only one thing left on the list (will it be the 'Eat Porridge For Breakfast' T-shirt?) and then the players' papers are examined to see who has the most correct things missing in the right order.

19 SAND SQUARE

A word square reads the same Across and Down. Use the words in the list to make three word squares each of which contain the word SAND

ANDY	DARK	PASS	SAND
AREA	IVAN	SAND	SIGN
ASIA	NEAR	SAND	VISA

WHAT DO YOU CALL A LADY ON A BROOMSTICK IN THE SAHARA?

A SAND–WITCH

20 WORDS WORST

These are games based on words. You do need a few people involved, all of them as daft as you.

* Make up a sentence containing as many words as possible that start with the SAME STARTER LETTER as the place you are heading for. Start each sentence with, "I'm going to". So, if you are heading for London, "I'm going to London to lead lots of lost left-handed leopards".

* Equally brain-boggling is the game where a word is chosen and the players have to make up a sentence in which each letter of the word, in turn, is used as the first letter of other words. eg: HULL could give Hurry Up Lazy Lad.

* Take the name of something you see then say it out loud BUT LEAVE OUT THE VOWEL LETTERS — that's a, e, i, o and u. Dog becomes 'dg', cat becomes 'ct' and station becomes the almost-impossible to say 'sttn'. The others have to decide what word you are trying to say (or else decide whether they should call a doctor at once!)

TRANS-FACTS
Half a dozen people have driven up Ben Nevis, Britain's highest mountain. It takes over seven hours to drive up but less than two for the return trip (still keeping the wheels on the ground).

---

21 CONE RANGER

We need a contraflow system . . . we need some road works . . . send for the CONE RANGER. It seems impossible to make any car journey without coming across rows of the dreaded plastic cones (even taking the car out of the garage).

Using 12 cones make a pattern in which there are six straight lines with each line containing FOUR cones.

WHEN IS A CORKSCREW LIKE A TRAFFIC JAM?

WHEN IT GETS IN A BOTTLE NECK

TRANS-FACTS
Traffic lights were introduced in London in 1868, but it was not until 1930 that it was against the law to disobey them.

22 TROUBLED TOURIST

Our tourist got very mixed up when he got back home and confused where many famous places were situated. Help him out by sorting out the phrases below.

1. Buckingham Palace is in FLORIDA
2. The Eiffel Tower is in SPAIN
3. Disneyland is in LONDON
4. I went skiing in PARIS
5. I saw a bullfight in SWITZERLAND

23 NATIONALITY LINK

Complete the phrases below by putting in the name of a nationality. The names you need are hidden in the word square and are written across, backwards, up, down or diagonally. You can use letters more than once but you don't have to use them all.

1 _____
   MEASLES
2 _____
   CHEQUERS
3 _____
   TWINS
4 _____
   WINDOW
5 _____
   DELIGHT
6 _____
   PASTRY

7 _____
   ROLL
8 _____
   STEW
9 _____
   RAREBIT
10 _____
   MUMMY
11 DOUBLE
   _____
12 _____
   ROULETTE

T	U	G	Y	P	N	E	I	S	H	C	S
E	U	R	T	I	S	E	H	S	I	G	I
G	E	R	K	A	N	W	I	H	E	R	A
Y	N	U	K	S	R	E	A	C	R	M	M
P	A	S	I	I	A	L	M	A	U	N	E
T	I	N	R	U	S	S	E	S	S	E	S
I	T	S	I	S	A	H	N	F	S	E	E
A	P	N	I	S	C	I	S	R	I	S	I
N	Y	W	A	T	M	E	S	I	A	W	S
G	S	I	U	S	N	E	F	R	N	S	I
E	A	D	M	A	E	S	R	I	S	A	H
N	E	D	M	U	T	C	E	Y	G	E	D
A	T	R	U	D	H	C	N	P	T	I	A
I	E	S	E	N	I	H	C	T	U	D	N
G	T	P	Y	G	E	H	H	S	I	R	I

24 PAIROPLANES

They may look alike, but only two of these planes are identical. Can you spot the pair?

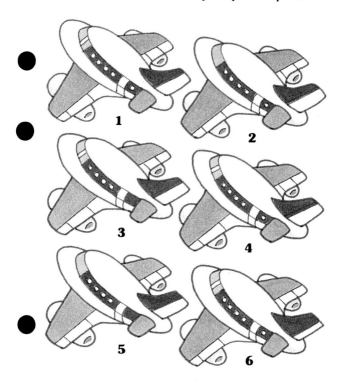

TRANS-FACTS
When Alcock and Brown first flew the Atlantic non stop, to put their name in the record books, they also shared a prize of £10,000.

25 AND THE CONSEQUENCE WAS . . .

For this game you need paper and a pencil for each player. Works with two players, but the more the merrier.

1. Write a name, fold the paper so no-one else can see then pass the paper on. Go clockwise if there are a few people.

2. Write where your person went to. Fold paper and pass on.

3. Write who your person met. Fold and pass on.

4. Write what they said. Fold and pass on.

5. Write where they decided to go to. Fold and pass on.

6. Write the 'consequence' or the ending of the adventure.

7. Each person takes a sheet of paper, unfolds it and reads out the 'story' it tells. There can be some very mixed-up meetings usually guaranteed to get a giggle.

26 MIXED UP MOUNTAINS

The names of hill and mountain ranges have had their letters mixed up and rearranged in alphabetical order. Can you sort them out?

1 CEIKORS

2 ADENS

3 EEENPRSY

4 AAAHILMSY

5 EEINNNPS

27 MEETING POINT

A car got on the M1 motorway at London and is heading north towards Birmingham, travelling at 40 miles an hour. Fifteen minutes later a car gets on the M1 at Birmingham and starts south towards London travelling at 55 miles an hour. The distance between Birmingham and London is 105 miles. Which car is nearer to London when they meet?

\boxed{28} **TRAVEL TRAIL**

Start at the letter top left and move one letter at a time. You can move in any direction except on a diagonal to spell out the names of five different European countries

3 WAYS TO CROSS THE ENGLISH CHANNEL...

BY BOVERCRAFT

SHOW DOGS TRAVEL BY HOVERCRUFTS

I CROSS BY HOPPER-CRAFT

I L Y A
T A S U
E D T R
N E W I
F E S A
R R I E
A N C E

\text{}

29 NUMBER CODE

Each letter which slots in to the frame has a number. We have given you two words with their number codes to start you off. Keep a record of which number represents which letter in the smaller grid, and find the words to fit the frame.

9	3	5	13	3	13		14		16	
11		24		1	15	3	16	8	13	
19	3	2	16	7	17		4		26	
3		19		3		1 **T**	2 **R**	3 **A**	4 **I**	5 **N**
4		3	11	5	1	4	8		21	
1	3	17		12		21		13	24	13
	4		23	8	2	9	4	5		15
22	2	3	11	12		8		24		8
	20		4		13	1	2	24	7	7
25	11	4	21	15	8			6		18
	13		8		3 **A**	2 **R**	10 **G**	17 **Y**	7 **L**	8 **E**

1 **T**	2 **R**	3 **A**	4 **I**	5 **N**	6	7 **L**	8 **E**	9	10 **G**	11	12	13
14	15	16	17 **Y**	18	19	20	21	22	23	24	25	26

TRANS-FACTS
In 1988, a group of Americans travelled 116 miles in 75 hours on tricycles — underwater!

30 LINX

Either a team game or can be played as a game of patience. Start with the place name of your destination, let's say GLASGOW. Now take the last letter of GLASGOW and think of a place name beginning with that letter. Carry on using the LAST LETTER of each word as the first of the next. Put a time limit on how quickly you have to answer if you are playing with friends.

TRANS-FACTS
Before the days of cars and trains, carriages pulled by four horses could travel at around 21 mph. The animals could only keep up this 'lightning' speed for about an hour.

---

31 WHAT AM I?

My first is in tree
But isn't in reel
My second's in free
But isn't in feel
My third is in bat
But isn't in bit
My fourth is in hit
But isn't in hut
My fifth is in rain
But isn't in rail
That should give you a clue
Are you now on the trail?

32 MAKE THE BREAK

Each group of ten letters can be broken down into TWO words of five letters. Words read from left to right and the letters are in the correct order. Can you make the break? There's a clue in each case

1 BECALCIFHF

_ _ _ _ _ / _ _ _ _ _

Seen by the sea

2 FYERACRHYT

_ _ _ _ _ / _ _ _ _ _

Two types of boat

3 GRAUARILSD

_ _ _ _ _ / _ _ _ _ _

Seen on or from a train

HOW DOES A BEE TRAVEL? . . . . BY BUZZ

. . . HERE'S A GOOD ONE . . . WHAT DO YOU CALL A MAN WITH A SEAGULL ON HIS HEAD? . . . CLIFF!

WHAT ABOUT THIS ONE THEN . . . . . . WHAT FLIES AND WOBBLES? . . . A JELLYCOPTER . . . HA HA!!

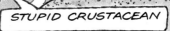

STUPID CRUSTACEAN

Coming in to land any moment, and here's a view looking down at the ground from up in the air.

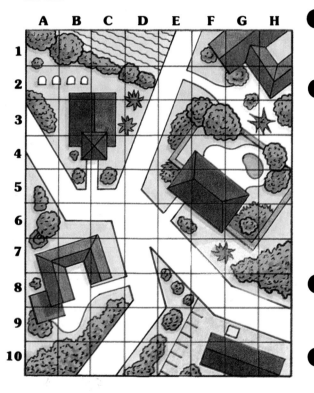

Which square on the scene matches up with the detail shown here?

34 WHEN IN ROME

A word square reads the same Across and Down. Use the words in the list to make three word squares each of which contains the word ROME.

ALTO	ENDS	ITEM	ROME
DEAR	FRED	MEND	ROME
EMMA	HAIR	OMEN	ROME

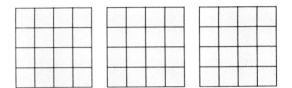

TRANS-FACTS
Motor cars may be very much part of the 20th century but 'fire carts' were written about in China as early as 800 B.C.

---

35 ALPHABET LIST

Either a team game or can be played as a game of patience. The idea is to spot objects that begin with letters of the alphabet . . . and in order. So you start with A for Aardvark (you mean you don't have one in the car) or whatever, then B and so on. You can look both inside and outside your vehicle. In fact you will need to when you get down to Z. This can help to pass a *very* long period of time.

36 ROUNDABOUT THE USA

Find the names of five places in the USA in the circle below. The last letter of one name is the first of the next.

TRANS-FACTS
A Frenchman drove his truck for nearly three miles at Silverstone on 17th August, 1986. Not much unusual about that, is there? Only the fact he was doing a version of a giant wheelie, and travelling along on ONLY TWO WHEELS.

37 FLYOVER

Can you find your way around the motorway junctions so that you can travel from home to the garage?

HOME

GARAGE

The names of five islands have had the letters of their names mixed up and rearranged in alphabetical order. Can you sort them out?

39 IN THE DISTANCE

We give you some journeys along with a list of distances. Try to match the correct distances to the journeys.

JOURNEYS

1 LONDON to GLASGOW
2 MANCHESTER to MOSCOW
3 DUNDEE to EDINBURGH
4 PARIS to TOKYO
5 JOHN O'GROATS to LAND'S END

DISTANCES

A 868 ml / 1,397 km
B 6,200 ml / 9,978 km
C 56 ml / 90 km
D 397 ml / 639 km
E 1,575 ml / 2,467 km

40 TRAVEL TRAIL

Start at the letter at the top left and move one letter at a time. You can move in any direction except on a diagonal to spell out the names of six countries.

```
T K E Y T
U R I N U
A G S I A
L U T R S
J F I O P
A N J P A
P A I N I
```

TRANS-FACTS
Until recently Egyptian driving tests were made up of two sections . . . driving six metres forward . . . then driving six metres in reverse. It was reckoned to be the world's easiest driving test.

41 CAR QUICKIES

Easy-peasey games for the car.

* Take turns trying to guess the colour of the next car to go past you in the opposite direction.

* Choose a number from 0 to 9. Try to spot your number on the plates of other cars. Score 1 point each time your number turns up.

* Fix a target someway in the distance. Close your eyes, and open them when you think the car has reached that object. Did you manage to judge the time taken to travel the distance?

DAD... I DON'T THINK YOUR'E MEANT TO BE PLAYING THIS GAME!

42 TRAVELLER'S TEST

Some quickfire travel questions.

1 What name was given to the 'Children' in the classic story by Edith Nesbit?

2 What kind of movement did Kylie Minogue sing about in her first big hit?

3 In the song about the 'Owl and the Pussycat', they travelled in something 'pea-green'. What was it?

4 What was 'The Flying Scotsman'?

5 We hear much of people running a marathon. Where does the name come from?

6 What is the nickname of the London Underground?

7 Which form of public transport will be mostly used in the Channel Tunnel?

8 In the cartoon 'Jimbo and the Jet Set' aeroplane Gloria is named after an airport. Which one?

9 At which London station was a marmalade-loving bear found?

10 For what invention is J.L. Macadam famous?

11 If you travelled by bus in Venice what would be odd about it?

12 What does the road sign mean which is triangular in shape with an exclamation mark in the middle of it?

13 Which is further north, Glasgow or Edinburgh?

14 Lufthansa, Pan Am and El Al are all names of what?

15 How many children are there on the road sign which warns that there is a school near?

43 TOWN HUNT

The names of towns and cities beginning with the letter 'M' are hidden in the word search. Names are printed in straight lines across, backwards, up, down or diagonally. You can use letters more than once but you don't have to use them all.

MADRID   MIAMI
MALAGA   MILAN
MANCHESTER   MINNEAPOLIS
MANILA   MONTE CARLO
MARSEILLE   MONTREAL
MELBOURNE   MONZA
MEMPHIS   MOSCOW
MEXICO CITY   MUNICH

M	N	M	O	N	T	R	E	A	L	H	M
E	A	E	N	A	S	M	N	X	I	C	C
X	S	D	P	I	O	E	R	I	C	I	H
I	O	I	R	L	C	I	U	T	Y	N	E
C	O	M	H	I	N	M	O	E	X	U	I
O	L	E	C	P	D	A	B	L	I	M	R
C	R	X	I	O	M	C	L	L	A	T	E
I	A	T	E	R	M	E	E	I	M	Y	T
T	C	E	M	A	M	N	M	E	M	I	S
Y	E	S	T	O	C	A	H	S	O	N	E
S	T	E	S	M	N	A	G	R	P	N	H
E	N	C	R	I	C	Z	N	A	A	E	C
H	O	M	L	H	I	I	A	M	L	L	N
W	M	A	N	M	A	M	S	U	N	A	A
C	S	I	L	O	P	A	E	N	N	I	M

44 MIDDLE OF THE ROAD

Write your answers in the grid Across. The middle letter of every word is 'A'.

1 Small lorry or truck
2 Aircraft
3 Caribbean island, capital Kingston
4 Nationality of someone from Budapest
5 Trailer, mobile home
6 Resort of Florida
7 Motor vehicle

TRANS-FACTS
The first ever flight in an aircraft was over a distance of 120 feet and a speed of 30 mph.

45 LET'S GO!

Find an answer to the quick clues that always begin with G O.

1 **Game played by Nick Faldo**
   G O _ _
2 **Character who visited the three bears**
   G O _ _ _ _ _ _ _ _
3 **Large white bird similar to a duck or swan**
   G O _ _ _
4 **Score in football**
   G O _ _
5 **Animal which has kids**
   G O _ _
6 **Precious yellow metal**
   G O _ _
7 **Opposite of bad**
   G O _ _
8 **Large ape**
   G O _ _ _ _ _
9 **Soft green fruit**
   G O _ _ _ _ _ _ _
10 **Farewell; word said when you leave somebody**
   G O _ _ _ _ _ _

> **TRANS-FACTS**
> The first sailing round the world took almost three years, from 20 September 1519 to 6 September 1522.

46 ON THE MOVE

● The ends of these words have been taken away, moved around and matched up with the wrong beginnings. Can you move things around again so that all words are reunited with their correct partners?

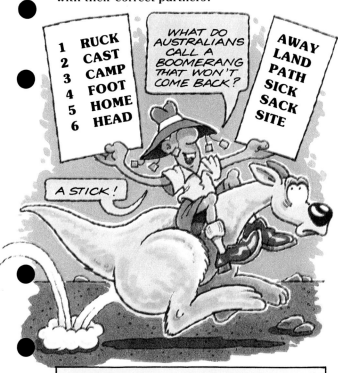

1 RUCK
2 CAST
3 CAMP
4 FOOT
5 HOME
6 HEAD

AWAY
LAND
PATH
SICK
SACK
SITE

WHAT DO AUSTRALIANS CALL A BOOMERANG THAT WON'T COME BACK?

A STICK!

TRANS-FACTS
The earliest boats are thought to have been used by Aborigines as early as 40,000 B.C.

47 CROSS COUNTRY

Rearrange each line of letters to spell the name of a country. Write the answers in order in the grid and the shaded diagonal will give the name of another country.

1	A	G	H	N	R	U	Y
2	A	B	I	I	L	O	V
3	B	E	G	I	L	M	U
4	A	C	D	E	I	L	N
5	A	D	E	K	M	N	R
6	A	E	G	M	N	R	Y
7	A	D	E	I	L	N	R

1						
2						
3						
4						
5						
6						
7						

Answers

1 Untidy Suitcase
1 Trainers 2 Tracksuit
3 Jeans 4 Swimsuit
5 Sweatshirt

2 Red For Danger
None. You spell IT with
letter i and t

5 Spot The Difference

4 Start The Car
1 Carburettor
2 Caribbean
3 Caramel 4 Caravan
5 Cardigan 6 Cartoon
7 Carnival 8 Carriage
9 Carry 10 Cart

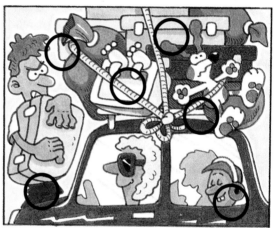

6 Number Code
Across: Ejects Avenue
Depart Plane Russia Get
Alp Brazil Duvet Ashore
Always Kitten
Down: Ending Export
Sat Bella Funnel Resort
Pizzas Equals Almost
Pigeon Began Ask

7 Stop Gap
1 Bus 2 Car 3 Sea

8 Placegrams
1 Athens 2 Dover
3 Ostend 4 Paris 5 Rome

10 Wheelie
19

11 Track to China
Track Trick Thick Chick
Chink China

12 Word Search

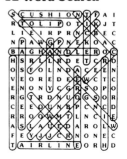

13 Off The Rails

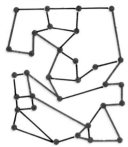

15 Roundabout the UK

Yarmouth Huntingdon
Nottingham Manchester
Rugby

16 Who Am I?

Pilot

17 Make The Break

1 Libya China 2 Corfu
Ibiza 3 Paris Milan

19 Sand Square

SAND PASS VISA
AREA ASIA IVAN
NEAR SIGN SAND
DARK SAND ANDY

21 Cone Ranger

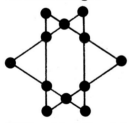

22 Troubled Tourist

1 London 2 Paris
3 Florida 4 Switzerland
5 Spain

23 Nationality Link

1 German 2 Chinese
3 Siamese 4 French
5 Turkish 6 Danish
7 Swiss 8 Irish
9 Welsh 10 Egyptian
11 Dutch 12 Russian

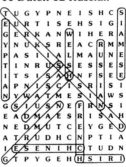

24 Pairoplanes

1 and 4

26 Mixed Up Mountains

1 Rockies 2 Andes
3 Pyrenees 4 Himalayas
5 Pennines

27 Meeting Point

Both the same distance
when they meet

28 Travel Trail

Italy Austria Sweden
France Eire

29 Number Code
Across: Kansas Thames
Warmly Train Auntie
Tay SOS Jerkin Fraud
Stroll Quiche Argyle
Down: Kuwait Norway
Sty Zaire Mexico Landed
Ticket Airbus Snoopy
Shelve Juice Sea

31 What Am I?
Train

32 Make The Break
1 Beach Cliff
2 Ferry Yacht
3 Guard Rails

33 Fasten Your Seat Belts
C 9

34 When In Rome
ROME FRED HAIR
OMEN ROME ALTO
MEND EMMA I TEM
ENDS DEAR ROME

36 Roundabout The USA
New York Kentucky
Yonkers Sacramento
Oregon

37 Flyover

38 Islandgrams
1 Corfu 2 Jamaica
3 Sicily 4 Anglesey
5 Iceland

39 In The Distance
1D 2E 3C 4B 5A

40 Travel Trail
Turkey Tunisia Spain
Portugal Japan Fiji

42 Traveller's Test

1 The Railway Children
2 The Locomotion
3 Boat
4 A train
5 It was a battle. A runner ran 26 miles 385 yards from Marathon to Athens to tell the news of victory
6 The Tube
7 Rail
8 Gatwick
9 Paddington
10 He developed a road surface covering
11 It would be a waterbus for travelling on the canals
12 There is a specific hazard
13 Edinburgh
14 They are names of airlines
15 Two

43 Town Hunt

44 Middle of the Road

1 Van 2 Plane 3 Jamaica
4 Hungarian 5 Caravan
6 Miami 7 Car

45 Let's Go!

1 Golf 2 Goldilocks
3 Goose 4 Goal 5 Goat
6 Gold 7 Good
8 Gorilla 9 Gooseberry
10 Goodbye

46 On The Move

1 Rucksack 2 Castaway
3 Campsite 4 Footpath
5 Homesick 6 Headland

47 Cross Country

1 Hungary 2 Bolivia
3 Belgium 4 Iceland
5 Denmark 6 Germany
7 Ireland HOLLAND